Steven Appleby

Bah!

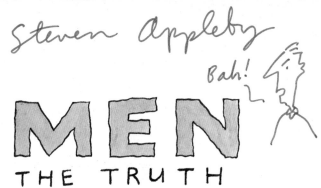

MEN
THE TRUTH

BEEP
BEEP B
BEEP
BEEP BEE
BEEP
BEEP BEEP
BEEP BEEP
BEEP
BEEP

LIE DETECTOR

Steven Appleby

BLOOMSBURY

for Nicola, Tom & Alfie.

THANKS To:
Jonathan Boatfield, Liz Calder,
Aldous Eveleigh, Mary-clare Foa, Kasper de
Graaf, Malcolm Garrett, Janny Kent,
Ben Murphy, Nicola Sherring, Rachel
Short... and all the men who have
inspired me.
Particularly special manly thanks to
George Mole who's contributions to an
earlier version of MEN THE TRUTH survive
on pages 80, 86, 87 and 103.

FIRST PUBLISHED in 1994
copyright STEVEN APPLEBY © 1994, 1995
The moral right of the author has been asserted

BLOOMSBURY PUBLISHING LTD, 2 Soho Square,
London W1V 5DE

ISBN 0-7475-2251-0

Printed and bound by Bath Press

AUTHOR'S NOTE:

This book is true of all men —
except me, of course.

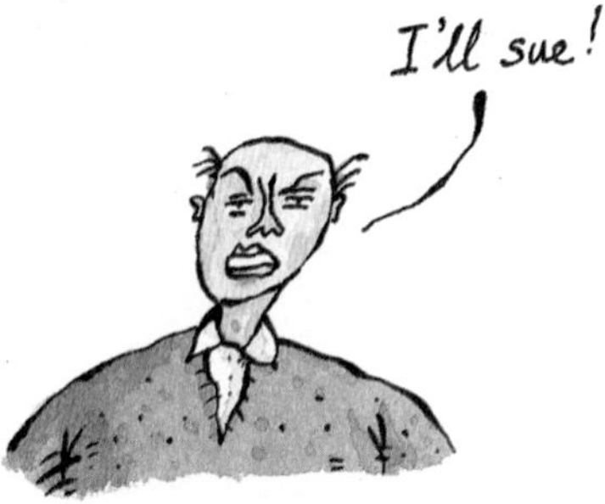
I'll sue!

They are helpful around the house.

They are always going to 'do it in a minute'.

They wash the dishes.

They change their clothes when they smell.

They only put their own clothes in the washing machine.

It's like magic! Clean, ironed clothes appear in my wardrobe each week!

They believe in the ironing fairy.

They overfill the rubbish bin.

They never lose anything — no. 1.

They wire up the plugs.

They never lose anything — no. 2.

Who's moved
the   *

*Insert your own favourite here.

They are full of helpful advice.

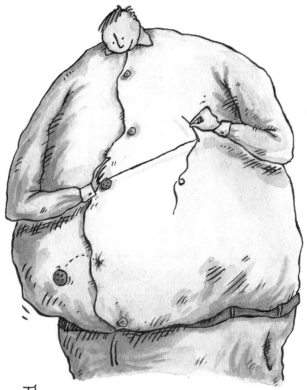

They can sew.

They never lose anything ~ no. 3.

They drive the car...

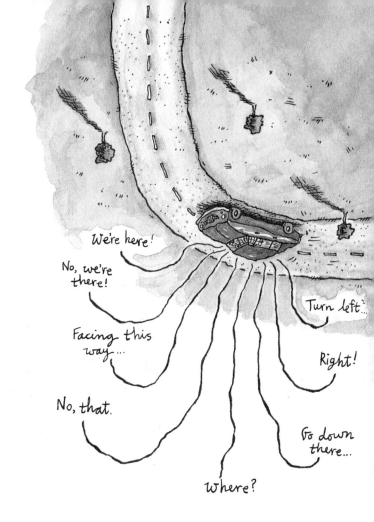

and they are better at reading maps.

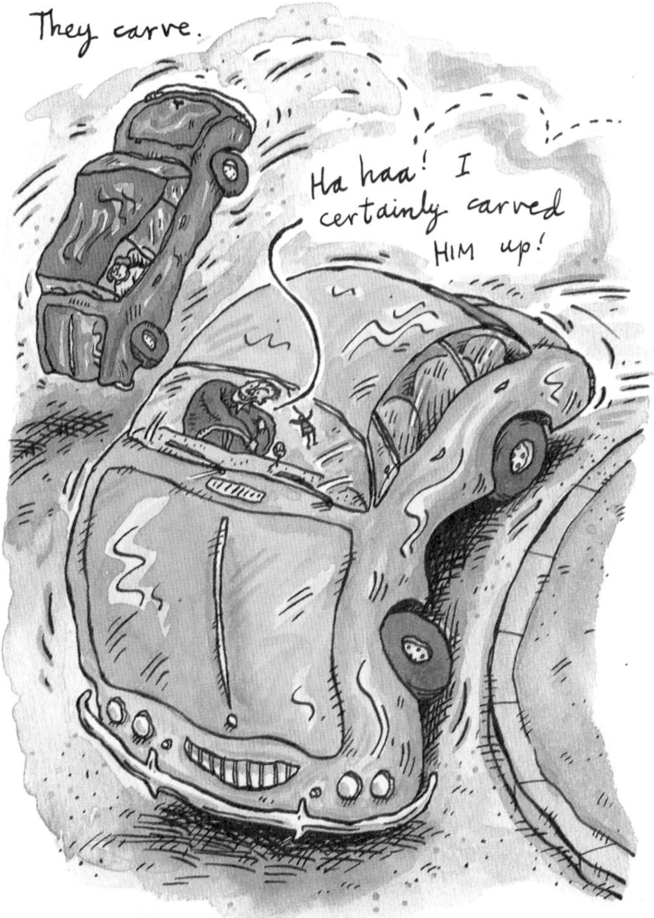
They carve.
Ha haa! I certainly carved HIM up!

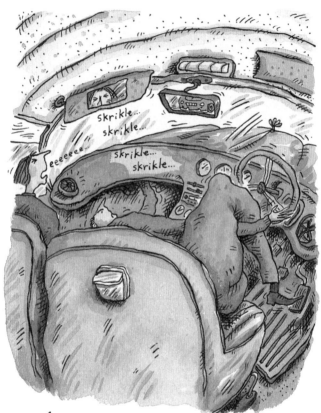

Rattles and squeaks drive them mad.

They are decisive.

They order in restaurants and they choose the wine.

I'll wait outside the shop while you try things on.

They yearn for the wide open spaces.

They have eyes in the back of their heads.

They can carry more shopping.

They don't make a fuss.

I warned you that would happen.

They can see the future.

They leave the seat down.

They have bicycles with crossbars.

They have a different way of taking
their pullover off.

They enjoy a game of chance.

They can always explain.

A DEVICE FOR READING A
MAN'S MIND:

They forget birthdays.

No I don't. Actually it's my birthday today.

They remember birthdays.

They need praise.

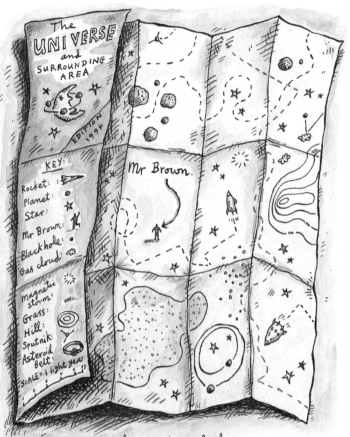

They are at the centre of the universe.

They never grow up.

They need a firm hand.

Who do you love most – mummy or daddy?

They need reassurance.

They love their mothers.

They get the biggest portion.

They discipline the children.

They are consistent.

They are supportive.

They are good at communicating.

It's never their fault ~ no. 2.

They show initiative.

They put women on pedestals.

They are the head of the family.

They feel secretly reassured by words like 'chairman', 'human', and 'mankind.'

Hello, dear...

Congratulations on becoming chairman.

They are openly disturbed by words like 'hysterectomy', 'gynaecology' and 'menstruation'.

They are sceptical.

They are patient.

A man with a particularly small and curiously-shaped penis.

A man with an inferiority complex.

They pretend to be bored in the
lingerie department.

They spend for consolation.

They are sceptical — no 2.

They buy thoughtful presents.

Four men indulging in man-talk.

There are some things they never talk about.

They sit with their legs apart.

Well... I'm not one
to boast... but I have to!

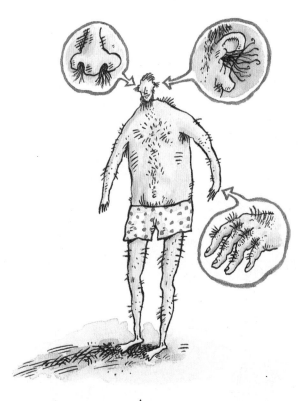

They are hairy.

Frank girl-talk makes them uncomfortable.

They are sexually imaginative.

They perpetuate schoolboy myths.

They like guns and cars.

They don't like being laughed at.

They have badly designed sex organs.

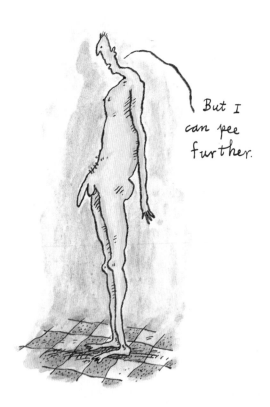

But I
can pee
further.

They wake up with an erection.

They are suspicious.

They won't sleep in the damp patch.

Prehistoric men grazing in a large herd.

They don't turn out to be handsome
princes.

THEY NEVER CRY — match the tragic events below to these five non-crying men:

A ~

B ~

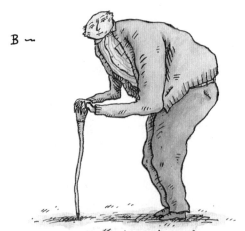

A's wife has just left him for a younger man.
B's wife left him for an older man.

C's wife has just told him she is leaving him for another woman, while D's boyfriend left him for a man with a bigger car. E recently left his wife in a black plastic bag at Paddington station.

They are territorial.

They adopt a philosophical attitude towards pets.

They are understanding.

They don't want to be tied down.

They wash their hair infrequently
and in the bath.

They comb across the bald patch.

They are manly.

They have noxious personal habits.

Darling, I know you don't want to watch the football so I've arranged to go and stay at Jims for two weeks on my own...
Aw, mum!
Waaaaaaa...
POP!
They are considerate..

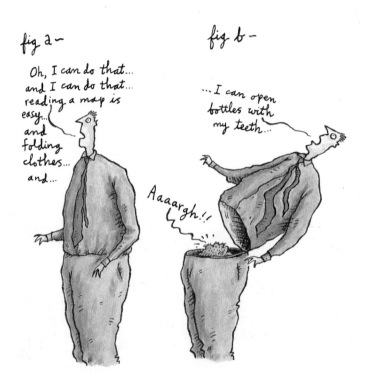

They are suspicious of holes.

They are terrified of spaghetti.

They look distinguished rather than old.

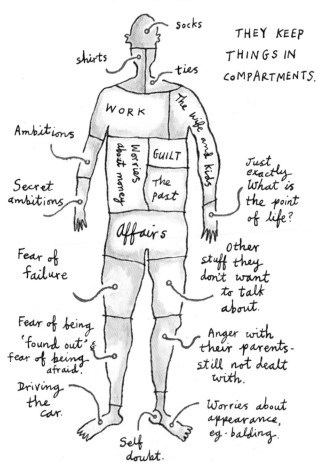

APPENDIX 2

HOW THEIR MINDS WORK:

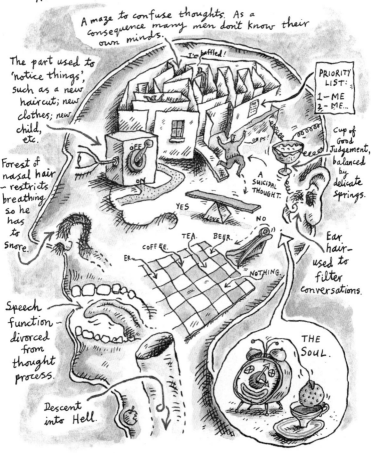

A maze to confuse thoughts. As a consequence many men don't know their own minds.

I'm baffled!

HELP!

The part used to 'notice things', such as a new haircut; new clothes; new child, etc.

OFF ON

Forest of nasal hair – restricts breathing so he has to snore.

PRIORITY LIST:
1 – ME
2 – ME...

OOPS

A SUICIDAL THOUGHT.

Cup of Good Judgement, balanced by delicate springs.

Ear hair – used to filter conversations.

YES

LOVE

NO

ER

COFFEE

TEA

BEER

NOTHING.

Speech function – divorced from thought process.

Descent into Hell.

THE SOUL.

Like their private parts, men's minds come in all shapes and sizes:

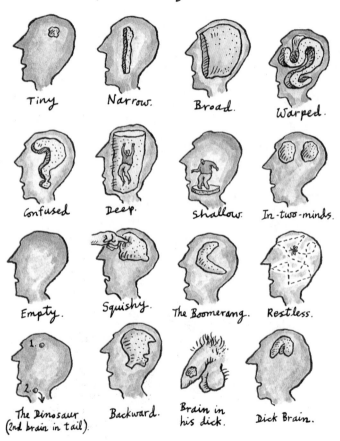

Tiny. Narrow. Broad. Warped.

Confused. Deep. Shallow. In-two-minds.

Empty. Squishy. The Boomerang. Restless.

The Dinosaur (2nd brain in tail). Backward. Brain in his dick. Dick Brain.

APPENDIX 3

MALE TYPES:

A Token Man. Can be redeemed for 10% off a new fridge.

A New Man. Guaranteed unused.

A Man with Two Faces.

APPENDIX 4

Some Ideal Partners:

i – A man asleep.

ii – A man not at home.

iii – A man watching T.V.